Poetry
and
Devotions
for the Soul
for Youth

Sandy Bohon LMHC

ISBN-13: 978-1-7325046-6-0

DEDICATION

This book is dedicated to my grandchildren, who have been a blessing in my life.

Katie, Braden and Leland

CONTENTS

God Loves All   4
How Wonderful Am I   8
Goodnight Prayer   12
The Singing Bird   16
The Moon that Shines   20
Zacchaeus   24
At the Park   28
Open My Eyes   32
God's World   36
Psalm 23   40
Read Your Bible   44
My Bike   48
Drizzle Goes the Rain   52
I Lifted Up a Rock   56
Choose Your Friends   60
School Today   64
The Pond   68
Playing in the Rain   72
Children are God's Gift   76
Take Time to Pray   80
Love is Like the Ocean   84
The Park   88
Armor of God   92
Monsters   96
The Wind   100

CONTENTS

The Sea Shore 104

God Made the Moon Above 108

Christmas Time 112

The World's so Big 116

Salvation 120

Politics 124

Jonathan's Journey 128

God Sent You 132

Garden – Weed 136

My Cat 140

Walking in the Woods 144

Clouds 148

Thunder Storm 152

Splashing in Puddles 156

Ten Commandments 160

Anger 164

Nature 168

1. GOD LOVES ALL

The stillness of the pond
   The raging of the sea
The blooming of a rose –
   And God made me.

The thundering in the storm
   The sky so wide and blue
The beauty of a butterfly –
   And God made you.

The coldness in the winter
   Leaves changing in the fall
The sun above so bright –
   And God loves all.

"Shortly before dawn Jesus went out to them, walking on the lake. When the disciples saw Him walking on the lake, they were terrified. 'It's a ghost,' they said, and cried out in fear. But Jesus immediately said to them: 'Take courage! It is I. Don't be afraid.' 'Lord, if it's You,' Peter replied, 'tell me to come to You on the water.' 'Come,' He said. Then Peter got down out of the boat, walked on the water and came toward Jesus. But when he saw the wind, he was afraid, and, beginning to sink, cried out, 'Lord, save me!' Immediately Jesus reached out His hand and caught him. 'You of little faith,' He said, 'why did you doubt? And when they climbed into the boat, the wind died down." (Matthew 14:25-32)

† † † † †

Have you ever been afraid? Some kids are afraid of snakes or spiders. Some are scared of thunderstorms or heights. Even adults become afraid when things happen to them.

Peter became afraid the morning he saw Jesus walking on water. Jesus told Peter to come out to Him, and he did. At first, Peter walked fine as he walked out to Jesus. When

Peter got his eyes off Jesus and saw the storm around him, he became afraid and called out to Jesus.

We may become afraid too, like Peter. When we look around at our circumstances, and things aren't going well for us, our fears increase. There are tests to take, sports events, and places we don't want to go. Everyone has problems in life, but where do you turn to for help? When we turn to Jesus and trust in Him, He will help us.

Dear Jesus,

When troubles come in my life, help me to trust in You. I know that You created the heavens and the earth and are all-powerful. You calmed the seas, and You can also calm me.

Amen.

2. HOW WONDERFUL AM I

Once was an inchworm,
   Crawling along,
Content as could be
   Singing his song,

"All of my friends are
   So very fast
But I see all details
   As I inch past."

Then up in the sky
   Flew a large bird
Soaring and singing
   His song could be heard.

"I'm so high up that,
   Rivers I see,
Mountains and forests
   Pass right under me."

So, if you're an inchworm
   Or a bird in the sky
God wants everyone to sing
   "How wonderful am I."

"Then people brought little children to Jesus for Him to place His hands on them and pray for them. But the disciples rebuked them. Jesus said, 'Let the little children come to me, and do not hinder them, for the kingdom of heaven belongs to such as these.'"(Matthew 19:13,14)

† † † † †

Are you like an inchworm or a bird flying high in the sky? Maybe you are neither, and you can describe yourself in another way.

We are all different. God created us all as individuals, and there is not another you on this earth. The Bible tells us that God is the potter, and we are the clay. He made each one of us exactly how He wants us to be.

We are also created with different abilities. Some people are good at drawing, and others are good at sports. Some people are quiet and keep to themselves. Others are outgoing and friendly.

Whatever your strengths are, you should build upon them and use them for the glory of God. We should try to improve our weaknesses and make them strengths. Some people say 'we are all a work in progress.' We all have areas that we can improve on. If you are good at art, then keep drawing. If you are good at sports, then keep practicing.

Jesus wanted the children to come to Him and not stay away. Jesus wants us all to come to Him and to have a relationship with Him. He accepts us just as we are. God loves each of us and wants us to celebrate our strengths and differences.

Dear Jesus,

Thank you for creating me the way I am. Help me to increase my strengths so that I can be stronger. Help me to recognize my weaknesses so that I can turn them into strengths. I pray that I can do everything for Your glory. Thank You for loving me.

Amen.

List below some of your weaknesses that you can work on.

List below some of your strengths that God has given you.

3. GOODNIGHT PRAYER

Lord, I thank You for this day
And the friends You sent my way.
For my family as they lay
In their beds, now I pray.

Thank You for the Word I read
For the stories to take heed,
But most of all for Christ You gave,
Who died for me, my soul, to save.

Thank You, Lord.

Amen.

"And pray in the spirit on all occasions with all kinds of prayers and requests. With this in mind, be alert and always keep on praying for all the Lord's people."(Ephesians 6:18)

† † † † †

Did you have a good day today? Did you go outside, or were you sick in bed? No matter how your day was, did you talk to Jesus?

When children are young, some parents will pray with them before they go to bed at night. When children get older, they tend to pray by themselves. Did your parents pray with you? Some families pray before dinner, and some don't. How does your family pray?

When you read your Bible, it is God talking to you. When you pray, it is you talking to God. The verse above says that we should pray for others. We should also pray many times during the day, not just before we go to bed. When we pray to God, we are telling Him about what is on our mind, and that we are trusting in Him to help us.

Our prayers can be precise or general. We can pray for our family members and friends, and we can pray for all the people in the world. We can pray for our church members and missionaries in other countries. When we get to know people, then we will know how to pray for them.

Things we can pray for others is when they are sick, going on a trip, or just for being our friend. We can thank Jesus for being our Savior. Jesus wants us to pray to Him, and He will bless us when we do.

Dear Jesus,

I know You want me to talk to You, and I want to talk to You, too. Help me to pray to You during the day, and help me to pray for others. Thank You for listening to my prayers.

Amen.

How often should we pray to Jesus?

List below some of the people you can pray for?

Pray continually.
Give thanks
in all
circumstances.

1 Thessalonians 5:17,18

4. THE SINGING BIRD

I wish I were a bird,
  Flying in the air,
I'd be up so high,
  Without a care.

I see children below,
  Smiling up at me,
Playing at the beach,
  Is what I'd see.

They're building castles,
  In the sand,
The best ones ever,
  In all the land.

And in the clouds,
  I want to fly,
Singing to Jesus,
  As I pass by!

"In that day you will say: 'Give praise to the Lord, proclaim His name; make known among the nations what He has done, and proclaim that His name is exalted. Sing to the Lord, for He has done glorious things; let this be known to all the world. Shout aloud and sing for joy, people of Zion, for great is the Holy One of Israel among you."(Isaiah 12:4-6)

† † † † †

Do you ever wish you could fly? If you could, where would you like to go? Do you have a birdbath or feeder in your yard? I love to sit on my porch and hear the birds sing. I live in Florida, and in the winter, there are lots of different birds in my back yard. Sometimes I watch them take baths in the pond in my yard.

Do you like to sing? Some people like to sing in the shower where no one can hear them. Some like to sing in front of others, or maybe in a choir. I wrote in another devotion about how God has given each person strengths and talents. If you sing well, you can bless others by singing for Jesus at church or other functions. If you play musical instruments, you can play in church or other

Christian gatherings.

The verses above are talking about singing praises to God for all that He has done for us. In Old Testament time, people played instruments and sang praise to God in the temple. Today we have pianos, organs, and other devices being played in church. In heaven, the angels are singing to God. When we are in heaven, we will also be singing praises to God. What a glorious day that will be!

Dear Jesus,

I can't fly now, but when I am in heaven, I will be able to. Help me to sing praises to You. I praise You because of all the wonderful things You have done for me.

Amen.

Has God given you the talent of a beautiful singing voice?

Do you like to listen to Christian music or music that talks about Jesus?

List below some of the things you can give praise to God for.

5. THE MOON THAT SHINES

The moon that shines above tonight
   Is shining over you,
And looking up I see its light
   Is shining on me too!

"He who forms the mountains, who creates the wind, and who reveals His thoughts to mankind, who turns dawn to darkness, and treads on the heights of the earth – the Lord God Almighty is His name." (Amos 4:13)

† † † † †

Do you ever stop and think that God reveals His thoughts to us? We know God has shown His power to us because we can see the moon above, and the clouds and trees. He also reveals Himself to us through the Bible. When reading Isaiah, Jeremiah, and other passages in the Old Testament, it says, "and the Lord said," which are His thoughts spoken to us.

In the New Testament, Christ is speaking and revealing His thoughts to us when He is talking to people. During the Sermon on the Mount Jesus is telling us how we should treat other people. We can see God's design through the universe that He created, and we can get a glimpse of His thoughts through His written Word.

God created the heavens and the earth, and He keeps it running smoothly. The earth keeps turning in space, and the moon keeps reflecting the light of the sun.

God created man to have thoughts and emotions. It is in our minds where our thoughts are formed that become our actions. In our physical bodies, we can be far from each other, but in our minds, we can be close and stay connected. We can think of our friends when they aren't with us and remember the things we did together.

Dear Jesus,

The Bible says, You reveal Your thoughts to us. I want to learn more about You. Help me when I am reading the Bible to understand You more.

Amen.

What is your opinion of God revealing His thoughts to you?

Next time you look up at the moon, think of friends that you haven't seen in a while. Write below some friends that you would like to see again.

6. ZACCHAEUS

I am a short man
   And I wanted to see
Jesus walk by
   So I climbed a tree.
As Jesus walked by
   He looked up and said
Take me to your house
   I want to be fed.
I climbed down the tree,
   As fast as I could
And invited Jesus home
   As everyone should.
No matter if you
   Are short or tall,
Jesus loves everyone
   Large or small.

"He wanted to see who Jesus was, but because he was short he could not see over the crowd. So he ran ahead and climbed a sycamore fig tree to see Him, since Jesus was coming that way. When Jesus reached the spot, He looked up and said to him, "Zacchaeus, come down immediately, I must stay at your house today." So he came down at once and welcomed Him gladly...

Jesus said to him, "Today salvation has come to this house, because this man, too, is a son of Abraham. For the Son of Man came to seek and to save the lost." Luke 19:3-6,9-10

† † † † †

Are you considered short or tall for your age? My son was short for his age in elementary and middle school, but then he shot up and is now 5 feet 10 inches tall. My daughter was short for her age and still is and she likes being short.

Zacchaeus wanted to see Jesus, but he had an obstacle, he was short and couldn't see over the crowd. So, he climbed a tree to see Jesus. We all face obstacles in life of one kind or another. Some have bigger obstacles.

Zacchaeus didn't let his shortness stop him from doing what he wanted to do. He wanted to see Jesus, so he climbed the tree. When obstacles come in your life, don't let them get you down. Find alternative ways to accomplish what you want to do.

The verse above says that the Son of Man came to seek and save the lost. Jesus wants all to come to Him to be saved. Zacchaeus sought out Jesus, and He saved him and his family. No matter what our circumstances, we can all seek Jesus, and He will save us.

Dear Jesus,

When I have problems in life, help me turn to You for help. I want You to be a part of my life. I want to seek You out and have a personal relationship with You. Help me through my obstacles in life.

Amen.

Are you seeking out Jesus?

List below any obstacles you may have in life, and how you can overcome them.

7. AT THE PARK

I went to the park early today,
With my friends, I went to play.
On the merry go round and round,
We all fell off and hit the ground.
On the swings, I went up high,
Until my feet could touch the sky.
We all ran around the tree,
I was so fast; they couldn't catch me.
Then when the sun is setting low,
And the moon looks down below,
When it's time to go inside,
To my home where I abide.
And at bedtime to Jesus, I pray
To thank Him for a lovely day.

"For this reason, since the day we heard about you, we have not stopped praying for you. We continually ask God to fill you with the knowledge of His will through all the wisdom and understanding that the Spirit gives, so that you may live a life worthy of the Lord and please Him in every way; bearing fruit in every good work, growing in the knowledge of God." (Colossians 1:9,10)

† † † † †

Do you enjoy going to the park and playing with your friends? Or playing outside? When I was young, I didn't have a park nearby, but I would ride my bike and play in the woods near my home. We would build forts in the tree in my back yard and had a great time. I lived a few blocks from the beach, and we would go there to swim and play.

Before I went to bed at night, I would pray to Jesus. Do you pray to Jesus at night before you go to sleep?

Praying is talking to God. He wants us to talk to Him and tell Him what is on our minds. We can pray to Jesus though out the day. He wants us to share the good things and the not so good things that happen to us. If we need help, we can pray to Him and ask for help.

Before going to bed at night is an excellent time to pray for your family and friends. While we are praying, we should thank Jesus for the blessings He has given us. We can thank Him for our family, friends, clothes, food, and shelter. We can thank God for the big things and the little ways He blesses us.

Dear Jesus,

Thank You for my family and friends. Thank You for the lovely day I had today. I pray that I have a good day tomorrow.

Amen.

Do you pray to Jesus every day?

List some of the things that you can thank Jesus for providing for you.

8. OPEN MY EYES

Lord, open my eyes,
Help me to see,
All the blessings,
You have for me.

Lord, open my mind,
Help me to know,
Your faithfulness,
That You bestow.

Lord, open my heart,
Help me to feel,
The love You send, and,
Your presence is real.

"Here I am! I stand at the door and knock. If anyone hears My voice and opens the door, I will come in and eat with that person, and they with Me." (Revelation 3:20)

† † † † †

Did you ever want to become friends with someone, but they didn't want to be your friend? You would invite that person to do things with you, but they didn't want to.

That is the same with Jesus. He wants us to have a personal relationship with Him, but we have to be willing to want one.

God did not create man as robots to serve Him; we have free will. It is our choice to trust Christ as our savior by faith. It is also our choice to serve Him. Christ will not break down our door but is patiently waiting.

Sometimes people don't realize all the things Jesus has done for them. They go around like a horse with blinders on. They can only see what is in front of them and don't take the time to take the blinders off and look around. Jesus has done a lot for each of us, and He wants to have fellowship with us.

Christ is knocking at our doors, and we are

the one who has to open it. In the New Testament, eating food with someone was an outward sign of brotherly love. Christ wants to have fellowship with you.

Jesus did not just die on the cross for our sins, He also wants to have a personal relationship with each of us. You have to be willing to open the door and let Jesus in. What better person could we have as our friend than Jesus who loves us.

Dear Jesus,

I believe that you died on the cross for me and paid for my sins. You also want to have a personal relationship with me. Help me to open the door to my heart and let you in so we can dine together.

Amen.

The verse above uses the illustration of Jesus standing at the door and knocking. What does that mean?

Are you willing to have a personal relationship with Jesus?

9. GOD'S WORLD

God is not in the rain
That hits my windowpane
Or in the clouds above
But He sends us His love.

God is not rocks or trees
Small ponds or raging seas
Nor hills or mountains high
Or rainbows in the sky.

And if you look outside
You'll see the world so wide,
Tigers and birds that sing,
God has made everything.

"God is spirit, and His worshipers must worship in the Spirit and in truth." (John 4:24)

† † † † †

Do you ever wonder where God came from? Most people do. We know that something cannot come from nothing, so how did God come about? The correct answer is that He has always existed. God does not have a beginning or an end; He is the 'I Am.'

Years ago, I used to think that God was sitting on His throne up there somewhere. But that is not true. When the Bible talks about God being on His throne, it is a figure of speech. When the Bible uses figures of speech about God, it helps us understand Him better. God does not have a physical body. He did come to earth in human form as Jesus to die on the cross for our sins.

The truth is God is a spirit. He is everywhere at the same time, but He is not in everything. We are not part of God and are separate from God. God created you and me, the universe, and everything in it. God knows our every thought, and everything we do.

We do not have to worship God in church or a place, but with our spirit, as He is spirit.

We cannot truly understand God, but God has revealed Himself to us through the things He has created, and through the Bible. The world is not chaotic but has order and design. The world and the universe run smoothly because God has set it in place.

We cannot see God, but we can see His effects through nature, and learn about Him through the Bible.

Dear Jesus,

Thank You for creating the universe and everything in it. Thank You for creating me, and loving me. Help me to appreciate what You have made.

Amen.

Where is God?

List below some of the things God created.

10. PSALM 23

The Lord is my Shepard, I lack nothing. He makes me lie down in green pastures, He leads me beside quiet waters, He refreshes my soul. He guides me along the right paths for His name's sake. Even though I walk through the darkest valley, I will fear no evil, for You are with me; Your rod and Your staff, they comfort me.

You prepare a table before me in the presence of my enemies. You anoint my head with oil; my cup overflows. Surely Your goodness and love will follow me all the days of my life, and I will dwell in the house of the Lord forever.

David wrote this Psalm in the Bible. He grew up as a shepherd, so when writing about Jesus being our Shepherd, he had first-hand experience. In other passages of the Bible, it describes people like sheep, and we need to be taken care of.

Have you ever walked along a creek or been at a lake? When the waters are still, it is peaceful. Sheep will not drink at fast-moving waters. Jesus leads us to the still waters so we can refresh our souls.

Jesus gives rest to the weary. He is the good Shepherd, and He guides us to where He wants us to be. He directs us along paths of righteousness and provides for our needs.

Jesus takes an interest in our day. When we go through dark and difficult times, He is there right beside us. He gives us the courage to live the life He has for us.

Christ also leads us to eternal life. He died on the cross for our sins, and whoever believes in Him will be with Jesus forever in heaven.

Psalm 23 talks about Jesus being the Good Shepherd who leads us and takes care of us. In what ways does Jesus take care of you?

11. READ YOUR BIBLE

Read your Bible
　　Every day,
And don't forget
　　To also pray.
Live good lives
　　And God will bless,
He will send you,
　　Happiness.

"Your word is a lamp for my feet, a light on my path." (Psalm 119:105)

"All Scripture is God-breathed and is useful for teaching, rebuking, correcting and training in righteousness, so that the servant of God may be thoroughly equipped for every good work." (2 Timothy 3:16,17)

† † † † †

Did you ever walk into a dark room, and stumble around because you can't see? Or step outside at night in the dark? You stand there because you don't know what is in front of you, and you don't want to bump into anything. Then you get a flashlight, and you can see where you want to go.

In life sometimes, we don't know in what direction we should go, and we feel like we are walking in the dark. God gave us His Bible to read to provide us with direction and understanding in our lives.

There are so many questions people have in life that are answered in the Bible. The Bible does not change. What was written thousands of years ago is still relevant for us today because God doesn't change. There is so much false teaching out there about God and the Bible that we should read it for ourselves to know the truth.

God created us, and He knows what is best for us. He didn't leave us in the dark but gave us the Bible so we would know how to live our lives. As the verse above says, the Bible is a light that guides us on our path in life. When we read the Bible and do what it says, we are on the path of light that helps us through the darkness.

Dear Jesus,

I pray that You help me to read my Bible every day so that I won't be in darkness. I want to learn about You in the Bible, and I want You to guide my day.

Amen.

Do you want to learn more about Jesus through the Bible?

12. MY BIKE

I went bike riding today,
   Over the paths, I flew,
Among the trees I road
   Under the sky so blue.

My bike is the fastest thing,
   Under the sun you'll find,
And when I ride with others,
   They're soon left far behind.

"Do you not know that in a race all the runners run, but only one gets the prize? Run in such a way as to get the prize. Everyone who competes in the games goes into strict training. They do it to get a crown that will not last, but we do it to get a crown that will last. Therefore I do not run like someone running aimlessly; I do not fight like a boxer beating the air. No, I strike a blow to my body and make it my slave so that after I have preached to others, I myself will not be disqualified for the prize." (1 Corinthians 9:24-27)

† † † † †

Do you like to go bike riding? When I was growing up, I would ride my bike all over the neighborhood with my friends. Riding bikes is good exercise and can help keep you healthy.

God gave us one body, and we should take care of the body God gave us. Exercising by riding bikes, running, playing soccer, swimming, and other sports are fun and keep us healthy. There are other things like eating well, and getting enough sleep at night that are also good for your health.

When people compete in sports, they have to be more dedicated to exercising. The verses above talk about training to run and compete in races. If a person didn't train, they would come in towards the end of the competition.

Christians are competing in a spiritual race in life. We should read our Bibles, pray, and do what Jesus wants us to do so that we can competitively compete in the race. When we do the things that we should do for Jesus, then we can win our race!

Dear Jesus,

I know that I am in a spiritual battle on earth. Help me to train so that I can win in the race, and not fall behind. Help me to be strong for you.

Amen.

What does it mean that we are in a spiritual battle on earth?

List some of the things you can do to compete in the spiritual battle we all face.

13. DRIZZLE GOES THE RAIN

Drizzle, drizzle goes the rain,
As it hits my window pane.
I want to go outside and play,
And not be in my room to stay.
I asked my mom, "what to do,"
And she said, "it's up to you."
So, I'll sit and think and ponder,
And let my mind go 'round and yonder,
And enjoy the drizzling rain,
That softly hits my window pane.

"You know when I sit and when I rise; You perceive my thoughts from afar. You discern my going out and my lying down; You are familiar with all my ways. Before a word is on my tongue, You, Lord, know it completely...For you created my inmost being; You knit me together in my mother's womb. I praise You because I am fearfully and wonderfully made; Your works are wonderful, I know that full well." (Psalm 139:2-4, 13-14)

When I was young, I grew up in Deerfield Beach, Fl. I lived a few blocks from the ocean. I loved going to the beach, and watching the waves hit the shore.

I also loved to sit by my bedroom window and watch the rainfall. It had a very calming effect on me. We didn't have computers, and we played outside almost every day. I remember making dolls and using small coconuts for their heads and sticks for their bodies. I drew pictures, sewed clothes for my dolls, and played ball in the field next door. Sometimes I would play cards or board games.

Today there are video games, cell

phones, and other electronic devices that keep a mind busy. Sometimes kids don't know how to enjoy the world around them. When they are not on their devices, or busy doing something, they get bored and don't like the feeling.

The verses above say we are wonderfully made. God knows our thoughts before we do. Next time it rains, sit and watch the rain, and think about how wonderfully God created you. Take a few minutes each day and enjoy your thoughts.

Dear Jesus,

I know that You said that I am wonderfully made by You. I get busy in my life and sometimes forget to talk to You. I pray that I will take a few minutes of each day and think about You.

Amen.

Do you enjoy watching the rainfall, or looking at nature?

Write below some of the ways that you are fearfully and wonderfully made by Jesus.

14. I LIFTED UP A ROCK

I lifted up a rock
  And what did I see
A little brown bug
  Looking up at me.

I tried to pick him up,
  But with a big hop
He jumped away
  Before I cried, "Stop."

"Therefore everyone who hears these words of mine and puts them into practice is like a wise man who built his house on the rock. The rain came down the streams rose, and the winds blew and beat against that house; yet it did not fall, because it had its foundation on the rock. But everyone who hears these words of Mine and does not put them into practice is like a foolish man who built his house on sand. The rain came down, the streams rose, and the winds blew and beat against that house, and it fell with a great crash." (Matthew 7:24-27)

† † † † †

My grandson used to collect rocks when he was younger. Do you have a rock collection or have ever collected rocks? There are all types and sizes of stones, and they are hard to destroy.

The verses above are talking about building our house on rock or sand. There are many types of foundations we can make our lives on. If we build our lives on the sand, we won't have a solid foundation. If we base our lives on Jesus and have Him as our foundation, we will be built on solid ground.

Everyone is continually building their house, whether it is flimsy and weak, or healthy and strong. When the wind is calm, if you have a flimsy house, it will stand. When big winds come, the flimsy house will blow away.

Jesus is known as the Rock in the Bible. That is why it is important to build your house upon the Rock. When we build our lives on Jesus, we will have stability in life. When troubles come, Jesus will help us through the storms of life.

Dear Jesus,

You created me, and know what is best for me. I want my foundation to be built on rock and not sand. Help me to build a stable house on You daily. When I have problems and troubles in life, help me to trust You to help me.

Amen.

Why should we build our lives on rock and not sand?

15. CHOOSE YOUR FRIENDS

A friend is like a path
They can lead you right or wrong,
They can tear your values down
Or help you be more strong.

A friend's words throw weight
Upon what you think or do,
So when you choose your friends
Think of their effect on you.

Will your friend help you grow
In morals and in the Lord,
For if they bring you down
Their friendship you can't afford.

So pray to God to send you
Good friends to walk beside,
And give you the courage
To cast others on the side.

"So Jonathan made a covenant with the house of David, saying, 'May the Lord call David's enemies to account.' And Johnathan had David reaffirm his oath out of love for him, because he loved him as he loved himself." (1 Samuel 20:16,17)

† † † † †

Having friends is important, and everyone wants friends. Some people have a lot of friends, and others have a select few. Either way, you have to make sure the friends you spend time with are a good influence on you.

God had chosen Saul to be the first king in Israel. Over time God wasn't pleased with Saul because he disobeyed what He had wanted him to do. God said that David would be the next king in Israel, and not Saul's children, which would be Jonathan. Jonathan knew he wouldn't be king over Israel and still loved David as his friend.

After King Saul and Jonathan had been killed in battle and David became king, he sought out Jonathan's son, Mephibosheth. David kept his word to his friend Jonathan and helped his children. Mephibosheth was crippled in his feet and could not walk, and God took care of him.

David and Jonathan were real friends and helped each other. We all have the desire to have friends, but we need to be careful of the friends we have. When a friend wants you to do something that you know is wrong, you should stand up for what is right. Saying something to your friend might make them reconsider what they are doing, and not do it.

We should choose friends that will help us grow spiritually in the Lord.

Dear Jesus,

I know that friends are important to me. I pray that You help me to find and keep friends that are pleasing to You.

Amen.

How would you describe the friendship between David and Jonathan?

List below the names of your friends. Are they friends that Jesus would want you to have?

16. SCHOOL TODAY

While I was in school today
The teacher was mean to me,
I went to Dan's desk to play
I brought him my car to see.

All the kids came to look...
Then the teacher stood up tall
Away from me my car she took
And I stood against the wall.

At home my mother said,
You need to listen and obey
So, I prayed to God in bed
To help me be good each day.

"I do not understand what I do. For what I want to do I do not do, but what I hate I do. And if I do what I do not want to do, I agree that the law is good. As it is, it is no longer I myself who do it, but it is sin living in me...What a wretched man I am! Who will rescue me from this body that is subject to death? Thanks be to God, who delivers me through Jesus Christ our Lord!" (Romans 7:15-17, 24-25a)

† † † † †

The boy in the poem did something in school he shouldn't have done. Have you ever done something you knew was wrong? Have you ever been in trouble in school? Sometimes kids do things accidentally and get in trouble. There are kids that purposefully do things they should not do, sometimes to make others laugh, or just to be disobedient.

Some people feel guilty when they do something little wrong. Others do lots of things they shouldn't do and don't feel bad.

The Bible says that because Adam and Eve sinned, we are all born with a sin nature. Paul wrote in the Bible in the verses above that he keeps doing things he doesn't want to do, even though he tries to be good. There is a constant battle in the Christian between doing right and wrong.

Have you ever told yourself that you weren't going to do that again, and then you did? That is what the verses above are saying, people, do things wrong when they try not to.

The Holy Spirit inside Christians comforts us, and He also helps us to know right from wrong. The Holy Spirit guides us and directs us to follow Jesus and live for Him.

† † † † †

Dear Jesus,

I try to be good, but sometimes I do things I shouldn't do. Help me to be good today and follow you.

Amen.

List below some of the things you do wrong that you want to stop doing.

17. THE POND

I went out to the pond today,
    To see what I could find,
My friend came along to play
    My sister, we left behind.

Some ducks were swimming around,
    They saw us, away they flew,
As they went homeward bound,
    Up in the sky so blue.

We saw some minnows swimming past,
    With our nets, we swooshed a lot,
Though they were so very fast,
    Many fish we still had caught.

Next time to the pond we'll bring,
    Our poles out far we'll cast,
And if we don't catch anything,
    Friendships we've made will last.

"But when she could hide him no longer, she got a papyrus basket for him and coated it with tar and pitch. Then she placed the child in it and put it among the reeds along the bank of the Nile. His sister stood at a distance to see what would happen to him. Then Pharaoh's daughter went down to the Nile to bathe, and her attendants were walking along the riverbank. She saw the basket among the reeds and sent her female slave to get it. She opened it and saw the baby. He was crying, and she felt sorry for him. 'This is one of the Hebrew babies,' she said." (Exodus 2:3-6)

† † † † †

Have you ever found something in the river? Can you imagine seeing a baby in a basket? That is what Pharaoh's daughter did.

In the Old Testament, it tells of how the Israelites were slaves to the Egyptians. Pharaoh wanted to destroy all the babies, so Moses's mother made a waterproof basket for him and placed him in the river. Moses's sister, Miriam, stayed by to watch what would happen to Moses.

Pharaoh's daughter came to the river

and found the basket and took it out of the water. Miriam said she could find someone to nurse him. Moses's mother took care of him until he reached the age to live with Pharaoh's daughter. Pharaoh's daughter called him "Moses" because she had drawn him out of the water.

Moses grew up, and later God used him to lead the Children of Israel out of Egypt to the promised land. Moses was one of the greatest men mentioned in the Bible.

† † † † †

Dear Jesus,

Thank You for protecting Moses while he was in the basket. I know that You also look after me and protect me. Thank You for loving me.

Amen.

How did Jesus take care of Moses?

List below some of the ways that Jesus takes care of you.

18. PLAYING IN THE RAIN

I love to hear the falling rain
As it hits my windowpane,
Or sometimes on the porch, I sit,
Until the pouring rain will quit.
But... If my mom says it's OK
Then outside in the rain, I play.
I love to wear my bathing suit
Without my raincoat or my boot,
'Cause then I'm free to jump and run
And slide in puddles, now that is fun.

"The Lord said to Moses, 'I have heard the grumbling of the Israelites. Tell them, 'At twilight you will eat meat, and in the morning you will be filled with bread. Then you will know that I am the Lord your God.' That evening quail came and covered the camp, and in the morning there was a layer of dew around the camp. When the dew was gone, thin flakes like frost on the ground appeared on the desert floor. When the Israelites saw it, they said to each other, 'What is it?' For they did not know what it was...The people of Israel called the bread manna. It was white like coriander seed and tasted like wafers made with honey." (Exodus 16:11-15,31)

† † † † †

Do you enjoy playing in the rain? When I was young, I loved playing in the puddles after the rain.

The children of Israel were slaves in Egypt for 430 years, and Moses led them out of Egypt to the desert. In the desert, the people didn't have any food to eat and grumbled against God.

God heard their complaining, and He fed them with bread out of heaven, which they called 'manna.' Psalms 78:24, talks about how God rained bread out of heaven to feed the people. Six out of seven days, in the morning the people would go out and collect the manna. On the sixth day, they would collect enough to eat for two days.

In the New Testament, it describes Jesus as the bread of life who came down out of heaven. As God fed the children of Israel's physical bodies with manna, Jesus feeds our spiritual souls with the Word.

Dear Jesus,

Help me not to complain. Thank You for coming from heaven to be the Bread of Life. Help me to see all the positive things You have done for me, and to appreciate what You have done.

Amen.

Why did God send manna out of heaven?

List five or more things you appreciate and give thanks to Jesus.

19. CHILDREN ARE GOD'S GIFT

Children are God's gift to us,
    To use and mold for Him.
And with the birth of a child,
    A new dawn is to begin.

"Children are a heritage from the Lord, offspring a reward from Him. Like arrows in the hands of a warrior are children born in one's youth. Blessed is the man whose quiver is full of them." (Psalm 127:3-5b)

† † † † †

"But Jesus called the children to Him and said, 'Let the little children come to Me, and do not hinder them, for the kingdom of God belongs to such as these.'" (Luke 18:16)

The Bible tells us that children are a gift from God. You are a blessing sent from heaven. You are unique, and there is no one else like you in the whole world. Just as every tiny snowflake is different, so each child is different.

God created the animals, but He made us different than the animals. God created us in His image and created us with a body, soul, and spirit.

No one should think that they are better than anyone else, because God created us all equal. No one picked who their parents are, or the color of their skin. These are things that we are born with and didn't have a choice in. Everyone should celebrate how they are similar and different from everyone else. As the song goes, God loves all the children in the world.

In the verses above, Christ's disciples thought Christ was too important to let little children see Him. Jesus rebuked his disciples and wanted the children to see Him. Jesus loves us all, no matter age or color, rich or poor. We are all equal in the sight of the Lord.

Dear Jesus,

Thank You for making me the way I am. Help me to appreciate the differences in others, because you made us all. Thank you for loving me.

Amen.

List below some of the ways you are similar and different from others.

20. TAKE TIME TO PRAY

Do not be too busy,
   Rushing through your day,
With many things to do
   And many things to say.

We need to take the time,
   To read God's Word and pray,
Then Jesus will bless us,
   And brighten up our day.

"Rejoice always, pray continually, give thanks in all circumstances; for this is God's will for you in Christ Jesus." (1 Thessalonians 5:16-18)

† † † † †

Do you ever feel lonely and wish you had someone to talk to? Maybe you argued with your friend, and feel confused? It is summertime, and all your friends happen to be away on vacation. You do have a friend that you can talk to, Jesus! He is always there, and He is ready to listen to you.

Friends talk to each other and share what is going on in their lives. If we quit talking to our friends, then over time we are not good friends any longer and become distant friends. That is the same with Jesus. If we don't talk to Jesus, then we become distant from Him. Praying to Jesus is the same as talking to Him. To feel close to Jesus, we should speak to Him often.

When we pray to Jesus and ask Him for something, He will answer us in one of three ways, yes, no, or wait. Sometimes our prayers are answered quickly, and sometimes it never happens. When we don't get our prayers answered the way we want, it could be that God doesn't think that what we want is the best for us, and He has something better. Other times God wants us to wait for a better timing of our requests. In all three types of answers, we need to trust in God that He knows what is best for us, and accept His answer.

As our earthly friends want to hear about what is going on in our lives, so does Jesus. The verse above says that we should be praying to God continually. We shouldn't leave our best friends out of our lives, so we also shouldn't leave Jesus out of our lives. When you have sad times or good times, take the time to talk to Jesus.

Dear Jesus,

Thank You for always being there for me, and wanting to talk to me. Help me to accept the answers You give to my prayers. Help me to speak to You more. Thank You for wanting to be my friend.

Amen.

Do you want to talk to Jesus more?

List below some of the things you can talk about with Jesus.

21. LOVE IS LIKE THE OCEAN

Love is like the ocean
Its depths cannot be known
But we can see
The gentle waves,
Upon the beach are blown.

"A furious squall came up, and the waves broke over the boat, so that it was nearly swamped. Jesus was in the stern, sleeping on a cushion. The disciples woke Him and said to Him, 'Teacher, don't You care if we drown?' He got up, rebuked the wind and said to the waves, 'Quiet! Be still!' Then the wind died down and it was completely calm. He said to His disciples, 'Why are you so afraid? Do you still have no faith?'" (Mark 4:37-39)

† † † † †

When I was a child, I grew up two blocks from the Atlantic Ocean in Florida and would go to the beach often. Sometimes the sea was so calm it looked like glass. Other times during hurricanes, the ocean was extremely rough, and the waves would break over the pier.

In the verses above, it tells about how

Jesus and His disciples were crossing the water. When they left the shore, the sea was calm, but a storm came up. They were afraid for their lives and woke Jesus up. When Jesus spoke, immediately the waves were calm.

Jesus's disciples were with Him every day and saw Him heal the sick and raise the dead. When the storm arose, they quickly forgot how powerful Jesus was and became afraid. That is how people can become, when problems arise, they forget that Jesus helps us.

We all go through rough times in our lives. When you do, do you turn to Jesus to help you? God loves you and wants to take care of you.

† † † † †

Dear Jesus,

I know that Your love for me is as deep as the ocean. Thank You for loving me.

Amen.

22. THE PARK

One of my favorite things
    On a hot summer day,
Is to go to the park
    With my friends and play.

On large slides, we go down
    On swings, we go high,
Tall trees we build forts in
    Up high in the sky.

Sometimes we just sit there,
    Content as can be,
Talking with our friends
    Under the shady tree.

And when the day is over,
    And it becomes too dark,
We know tomorrow will bring
    Another day at the park.

"David said to the Philistine, 'You come against me with sword and spear and javelin, but I come against you in the name of the Lord Almighty, the God of the armies of Israel, whom you have defied.'...As the Philistine moved closer to attack him, David ran quickly toward the battle line to meet him. Reaching into his bag and taking out a stone he slung it and struck the Philistine on the forehead. The stone sank into his forehead, and he fell face down on the ground." (1 Samuel 17:45, 48-49)

† † † † †

When you go to the park and play with your friends, do you pretend that you are a superhero? Do you sometimes pretend that you are fighting giants, dragons, or can fly? Maybe you pretend you are a princess and are looking for Prince Charming. It is fun to make-believe to be things that we aren't when we are playing. Maybe you don't pretend any longer but did in the past.

David wasn't pretending when he fought against Goliath, the Philistine. Goliath was like a giant because he was over 9 feet tall. David was probably a teenager or young adult when he fought against him. Goliath had a sword and spear, and David fought against him with a stone and a sling.

The nation of the Philistines was fighting against Israel. David fought against Goliath because he was disrespecting God. It took courage for him to fight against Goliath. God helped David in the battle because he trusted in Him. When we trust in God, we can overcome large obstacles in our lives. As Jesus helped David, He will help you too, when you trust in Him.

Dear Jesus,

Help me to trust in You to fight my battles. Help me to stand up for You when others disrespect You. Thank you for always being there for me when I need You.

Amen.

How was David able to win against the giant, Goliath?

Do you trust in God to help you fight your battles?

Write below some of the things that you pretend to be, or have in the past. Maybe you can draw a picture of how you looked.

23. ARMOR OF GOD

"Finally, be strong in the Lord and in His mighty power. Put on the full armor of God, so that you can take your stand against the devil's schemes. For our struggle is not against flesh and blood, but against the rulers, against the authorities, against the powers of this dark world and against the spiritual forces of evil in the heavenly realms. Therefore put on the full armor of God, so that when the day of evil comes, you may be able to stand your ground, and after you have done everything, to stand. Stand firm then, with the belt of truth buckled around your waist, with the breastplate of righteousness in place, and with your feet fitted with the readiness that comes from the gospel of peace. In addition to all this, take up the shield of faith, with which you can extinguish all the flaming arrows of the evil one. Take the helmet of salvation and the sword of the Spirit, which is the Word of God. And pray in the Spirit on all occasions with all kinds of prayers and requests. With this in mind, be alert and always keep on praying for all the Lord's people." (Ephesians 6:10-18)

The Bible explains that Christians are in a spiritual battle. Satan is the father of lies and deceives the world. We cannot fight this battle on our own, but with God's help. We need to fight this spiritual battle with the whole armor of God.

The "belt of truth" represents how we are to be honest and truthful in our relationships with others. The "breastplate of righteousness" comes from Christ. We are to stand up for truth and for what is right and to fight against what is wrong.

Our feet are to be fitted with the "gospel of peace." When we walk along the path of life, obstacles and conflicts will come our way. Peace is trusting in Jesus to help us. The "shield of faith" protects us from the lies that Satan throws at us.

We put on the "helmet of salvation" when we trust Jesus Christ as our Savior. We need to protect our minds from worshiping false gods and idols. The 'sword of the Spirit" is the Word of the Lord. Reading the Bible, knowing what it says, and applying it to our lives keeps us on the right path in life.

Dear Jesus,

I know that we are in a spiritual battle. Help me to put on the whole armor of God so that I can fight in this spiritual battle.

Amen.

Match below the Armor of God with the figure on the right.

A. Belt of Truth

B. The Shield of Faith

C. The Helmet of Salvation

D. The Breastplate of Righteousness

E. Feet prepared with the Gospel of Peace
   The Belt of Truth

F. The Sword of the Spirit

24. MONSTERS

I looked under my bed,
   And what did I see?
An ugly monster,
   Looking up at me.
I called my mom
   And she looked too!
She shook her head
   And it was true.
No monster was there,
   It was in my mind.
Looking again
   I could not find,
A monster there
   Or anywhere.
So if you're afraid
   Of things not there,
Then talk to Jesus
   And say a prayer.
He will keep you,
   Safe each night,
Then close your eyes,
   Goodnight, sleep tight.

"Do not be anxious about anything, but in every situation, by prayer and petition, with thanksgiving, present your requests to God. And the peace of God, which transcends all understanding, will guard your hearts and your minds in Christ Jesus." (Philippians 4:6,7)

"For I am convinced that neither death nor life, neither angels nor demons, neither the present nor the future, nor any powers, neither height nor depth, nor anything else in all creation, will be able to separate us from the love of God that is in Christ Jesus our Lord." (Romans 8:38,39)

Are you afraid of the dark? There are a lot of people that are. There are other things that people are afraid of, too. Such as taking tests at school, flying on airplanes, meeting new people, or going places they haven't gone before.

Jesus is aware of your fears and gives us verses in the Bible that tell us not to worry.

When we are afraid, we are to pray to God to comfort us. Jesus will comfort our hearts and give us peace.

Also, the verses above state that nothing can separate us from the love of God that is in Christ.

God wants you to trust Him to help you and take care of you. He wants you to have a good night's sleep and rest peacefully. God, who created the heavens and the earth, can take care of you so you should not fear.

Dear Jesus,

There are things that I am afraid of, but I want Your help. I pray that you will take my fears away. I want to trust You when I am afraid. Please help me trust in You.

Amen.

What do the verses above say about Jesus helping us?

List below some of the things you are afraid of, or times when you are afraid. How can you overcome your fears?

25. THE WIND

The wind was blowing,
   In my hair,
Tossing it around,
   Here and there.
Silently it comes from
   Who knows where,
Softly if blows
   Without a care.

"And I will ask the Father, and He will give you another advocate to help you and be with you forever – the Spirit of truth. The world cannot accept Him, because it neither sees Him nor knows Him. But you know Him, for He lives with you and will be in you." (John 14:16,17)

It is nice to be outside when the wind is gently blowing on a hot summer day. We don't see the wind, but we can see the leaves softly falling. We cannot see the wind, but we know it is there. That is the same as the Holy Spirit.

The word "Trinity" does not appear in the Bible but refers to the Father, Son, and Holy Spirit as one. They are equal in divine nature, essence, and attributes. To try and illustrate the Trinity, we will use the egg. It is made up of three parts, the white, the yoke, and the shell. The three parts represent God the Father, God the Son, and God the Holy Spirit. Each is God, yet there are not three Gods but one God.

When Christ went up to heaven, He said he would send the Holy Spirit as a comforter.

Today when someone trusts Christ as their Savior, they immediately become indwelt with the Holy Spirit.

Most of our earthly comforts are outside the body. The Holy Spirit is different. He indwells us to comfort us. He is a faithful guide, restrains us when we step into danger and soothes our souls when we are disheartened. The world does not know Him or see Him, but the Holy Spirit helps and comforts Christians.

Dear Jesus,

I have believed that You died on the cross for my sins, and I am saved. I know the Holy Spirit dwells inside of me. Help me to listen to the Holy Spirit when He guides me, directs me, and comforts me.

Amen.

What does "Trinity" mean?

Write below how the Holy Spirit helps you.

26. THE SEA SHORE

I love hunting seashells,
   Early at the shore,
When the sun is rising
   I love to explore.

Some of the shells are common,
   They are found everywhere
Some of the shells are treasures
   And extremely rare.

I love to hear the ocean waves,
   Breaking everywhere,
And to see the seagulls
   Flying in the air.

And when I'm home again,
   The shore is left behind,
I put the shells to my ear, and,
   I'm back there in my mind.

"When the queen of Sheba heard about the fame of Solomon and his relationship to the Lord, she came to test Solomon with hard questions. Arriving at Jerusalem with a very great caravan – with camels carrying spices, large quantities of gold, and precious stones – she came to Solomon and talked with him about all that she had on her mind. Solomon answered all her questions; nothing was too hard for the king to explain to her....(Queen of Sheba said) How happy your people must be! How happy your officials, who continually stand before you and hear your wisdom! Praise be to the Lord your God, who has delighted in you and placed you on the throne of Israel." (1 Kings 10:1-2, 8-9a)

† † † † †

Have you ever been on vacation and went to the ocean? Perhaps you have been on a cruise. Maybe you didn't go to the ocean, but you have been to other places on vacation. Sometimes people take back souvenirs as a reminder of the time they spent there. They also have memories of the things they did together with family and friends.

King Solomon was king in Israel and was

the son of David. God had made Solomon the wisest man on earth, and also very wealthy. Queen of Sheba heard of Solomon, and she traveled a great distance to visit him.

The Queen of Sheba had lots of questions for King Solomon. They talked about the Lord, and she was very impressed. The Queen of Sheba enjoyed her talk with King Solomon. She took the knowledge of God back with her and told others about the Lord.

† † † † †

Dear Jesus,

Thank You for the memories I have with my family. Thank you for letting me learn about You. Help me to tell my friends about You.

Amen.

Why did the queen of Sheba want to visit King Solomon?

Write about some of the good memories you have going traveling with your family.

27. GOD MADE THE MOON ABOVE

God made the moon above,
   And the stars to shine at night,
By day He made the sun to rise,
   To give us heat and light.

God made the rain to fall,
   To water the plants and trees,
God made the cats and dogs,
   And butterflies, birds, and bees.

Everything you see was made,
   By God up high above,
And He wants you to know
   He also sends His love.

"Then the Lord spoke to Job out of the storm. He said... 'Where were you when I laid the earth's foundation: Tell me, if you understand. Who marked off its dimensions? Surely you know! Who stretched a measuring line across it? On what were its footings set, or who laid its cornerstone – while the morning stars sang together and all the angels shouted for joy? Who shut up the sea behind doors when it burst forth from the womb, when I made the clouds its garment and wrapped it in thick darkness, when I fixed limits for it and set its doors and bars in place, when I said, 'this far you may come and no farther; here is where your proud waves halt'? Have you ever given orders to the morning, or shown the dawn its place?'" (Job 38:1,4-12)

† † † † †

Do you know someone who thinks that they are better than everyone else? These people are not humble. Being humble is a good thing.

Some people think they are the center of the universe, but they aren't. God was talking to Job in the verses above and asking where he was when God created the heavens and earth. None of us were born when the heavens and earth were created.

We cannot make the sun rise or set. We cannot make clouds go across the sky. God created the earth and boundaries for the ocean waves. God gives order into the world and keeps it running smoothly. He created the world and nature for us to enjoy. But we are not the center of the universe, God is.

Dear Jesus,

Thank you for creating the heavens and earth, and keeping everything running smoothly. You love me, and I am your child. Help me to stay humble and keep my life in perspective.

Amen.

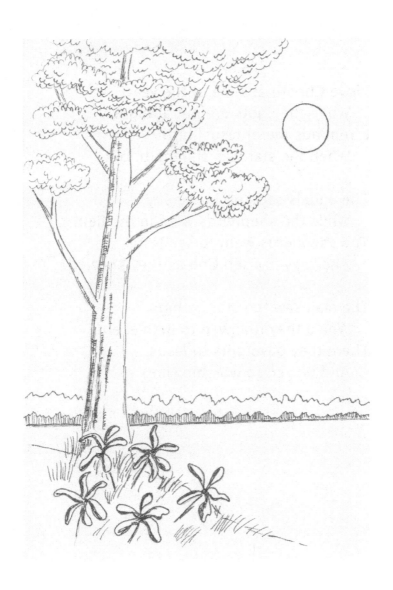

28. CHRISTMAS TIME

I love Christmas time of the year,
  When the lights are out at night,
It reminds me of Jesus' birth
  When the star was shining bright.

The angels sang up in the sky
  While the shepherds were in the field.
The shepherds went to see Jesus,
  And they praised God as they kneeled.

The Maji saw the star up high,
  Which they followed to Bethlehem.
There they gave gifts to Jesus,
  And bowed to worship Him.

"While they were there, the time came for the baby to be born, and she gave birth to her firstborn, a son. She wrapped Him in cloths and placed Him in a manger, because there was no guest room available for them. And there were shepherds living out in the fields nearby, keeping watch over their flocks at night. An angel of the Lord appeared to them, and the glory of the Lord shone around them, and they were terrified. But the angel said to them, 'Do not be afraid. I bring you good news that will cause great joy for all the people. Today in the town of David a Savior has been born to you; He is the Messiah, the Lord.'" (Luke 2:6-11)

When I was growing up, Christmas was my favorite time of the year. I loved to see the lights blinking and the smell of the Christmas tree. My dad would drive us around at night, and we would look at all the houses that were beautifully decorated. I looked forward to opening gifts in the morning and having Turkey and stuffing for dinner.

The true meaning of Christmas is celebrating the birth of Jesus. Jesus was born and placed in the manger. He was God in human form, the Messiah. It was prophesied in the Old Testament that the Messiah would come, and when Jesus was born, Angels proclaimed His birth.

We celebrate Christmas to remember the birth of Jesus. Just as the Maji gave gifts to Jesus, so we give presents to each other in celebration of Christ's birth. As we celebrate Christmas, let us not forget its true meaning, the birth of Jesus.

Dear Jesus,

Thank You for being born as a baby. You came to earth to die on the cross for our sins. When we celebrate Christmas, I pray that we think about You, and all the wonderful things You do for us.

Amen.

What is the true meaning of Christmas?

Write down some of your favorite Christmas memories.

29. THE WORLD'S SO BIG

The world's so big
   And I'm so small,
The mountains large
   And fir trees tall.
The flowers wave
   Among the weeds,
And both are blown
   New life of seeds.
The lions roar
   While tigers pounce,
And streams flow free
   Glistening with dance.
And God does watch
   From up above
And showers us all,
   With His love.

"'Here is a boy with five small barley loaves and two small fish, but how far will they go among so many?'" Jesus said, 'Have the people sit down.' There was plenty of grass in that place, and they sat down (about five thousand men were there). Jesus then took the leaves, gave thanks, and distributed to those who were seated as much as they wanted. He did the same with the fish. When they had all had enough to eat, He said to His disciples, 'Gather the pieces that are left over. Let nothing be wasted.' So they gathered them and filled twelve baskets with the pieces of the five barley loaves left over by those who had eaten." (John 6:9-13)

† † † † †

Do you sometimes feel small and unimportant? You may feel that you can't make a difference to others. Maybe you feel sad because you can't run as fast as others, or you aren't as smart as others.

The boy in the Bible did make a difference. We don't know how the boy in the verses above felt, but we do know that Jesus used him.

There were about 5,000 men, not

including the women and children that came to hear Jesus speak that day, and they were hungry. Jesus felt sorry for the crowd and wanted to feed them. Jesus took the boy's bread and fish and performed a miracle and fed them all.

God made us each unique and different. We all have gifts and talents that can be used by God. The boy willingly gave his bread and fish to Jesus. Are you willing to be used by God?

Dear Jesus,

I know that you love me and are taking care of me. I want to help others. Help me to be used by You by helping others.

Amen.

How do you think the boy felt when Jesus used his fish to feed all the people?

Write below ways Jesus can use you.

30. SALVATION

I am so happy
   Can't you see,
Because I have Jesus
   Living in me.

I have believed
   He died for me,
I'll be with Him,
   Eternally.

"For God so loved the world that He gave His one and only Son, that whoever believes in Him shall not perish but have eternal life." (John 3:16)

† † † † †

Do you ever wonder where you will go when you die? You don't have to wonder any longer because the Bible says you can know you have eternal life if you trust Jesus as your Savior.

Do you know what sin is? The Bible says that every time we do something we shouldn't do, that we are sinning. A lot of times we sin without even realizing it when we have bad thoughts or are mean to our family members.

Some people think that good people go to heaven and bad people don't, but the Bible says that we are all sinners and we all do things wrong. We cannot enter heaven with sin on us. No matter how good we are, we are still sinners and do things we shouldn't do.

The Bible says that being good does not take away our sin. For example, reading our Bibles, praying, doing nice things for others won't take away our sin.

God did make a way for each one of us

to go to heaven. He sent His son Jesus Christ to die on the cross for our sins in our place. We are saved by what Jesus did, not by what we do. When we trust Jesus as our Savior, our sins are washed away. Then we can go to heaven someday and be with Jesus forever. Isn't it nice to know you are going to heaven?

† † † † †

Dear Jesus,

I believe that You died on the cross for my sins. I want to go to heaven one day, and I am trusting You to get me there. Thank you for dying on the cross for my sins.

Amen.

Salvation is not what we do but what Jesus did for us on the cross. Have you trusted Jesus as your Savior?

31. POLITICS

I am just a kid
   Politics are not for me
I want to go outside
   And play happily.

But my mom said to me,
   You need to understand
What is going on, now,
   The happenings in the land.

So, when things are good or bad,
   You'll make an informed choice
And help others to see
   That everyone has a voice.

"Now the king was attracted to Esther more than to any of the other women, and she won his favor and approval more than any of the other virgins. So he set a royal crown on her head and made her queen instead of Vashti." (Esther 2:17)

† † † † †

Have you ever pretended that you were a princess, prince, king, or queen? Have you ever dressed up and pretend you were famous? Sometimes kids will act out a part in a stage play and be royalty.

In the Old Testament, there is a book called Esther. It is a true story about a king named Xerxes who ruled over many people. King Xerxes got upset with his wife, Queen Vashti, and said she could no longer be queen, and he searched for another woman to take her place. Beautiful women came from all over the country wanting to be queen.

There was a young woman named Esther, whose relative, Mordecai, had raised her, and they were Jewish. Of all the women wanting to be queen, Xerxes chose Esther to be his queen.

There was a problem in the court. Haman

was the number one person under King Xerxes, and he deceived the king into wanting to kill the Jewish people in his land. Xerxes did not know that Esther was Jewish. Mordecai found out the plot and had Esther ask the king not to take the lives of her and her people.

Esther was nervous about going before the king and had all the Jewish people pray for her. Then she went before King Xerxes and asked him not to kill her people, and he listened to her. Esther used her voice to save the Jewish people in the land.

Dear Jesus,

I know we all have a voice that we can use to help others. I want to be strong like Esther. Help me to get involved in the lives of others. Please help me to use my voice for You.

Amen.

How did Esther use her voice to help others?

Write down some things you can do to help others.

32. JONATHAN'S JOURNEY

Our God in the heavens
　　Only he knows,
In this great country,
　　Where Jonathan goes.

He's on a journey
　　From the east to the west,
The sky is his window,
　　The ground is his rest.

And while he is gone,
　　To God, I will pray,
That He keeps him safely
　　And blesses his way.

"It was also called Mizpah, because he said, 'May the Lord keep watch between you and me when we are away from each other." (Genesis 31:49)

† † † † †

Have you ever taken a trip on a motorcycle? I have a friend that made a motorcycle trip and he road through every state in America, except Hawaii. It took him about one year to complete his journey. He went from Key West to Alaska and every state in between. He would sleep in a tent at night. I wrote this poem about him while he was away.

In the Old Testament, Jacob spent 20 years working for his father in law, Laban, but things didn't turn out well. God told Jacob to go back to his home country, which is now Israel. Jacob fled quickly with his wives and children to go to his home country because he was afraid of Laban.

Laban chased after Jacob when he found out that he had left. At night, God spoke to Laban and told him not to say anything good or bad to Jacob.

When Jacob and Laban met, there was contention between them, because Laban was upset with Jacob. They talked and came to a friendly agreement. The place has since been called Mizpah.

The original use of the word Mizpah meant 'safeguard and warning.' The meaning has changed over time to be a 'beacon or watchtower.' God is our watchtower watching over us when we are separated from one another. When our friends or family members go on vacation, we should pray for them, that God will bring them safely home.

Dear Jesus,

I pray that You take care of my family when we are on vacation. I pray that You watch over my friends when they are away and that You bring them safely home. Thank You for taking care of us.

Amen.

Have you ever been on a journey or vacation?

Write below what Mizpah means, and how you can use it.

33. GOD SENT YOU

God holds the world
    In His hand,
And sends the rain
    To little flowers,
Has touched my life
    By sending you,
    To brighten up
All my tomorrows.

"How, then, can they call on the one they have not believed in? And how can they believe in the one of whom they have not heard? And how can they hear without someone preaching to them? And how can they preach unless they are sent? As it is written, 'How beautiful are the feet of those who bring good news!'" (Romans 10:14,15)

† † † † †

Do you have a friend that you like to spend time with? Do you look forward to them coming over, or going to the park with him or her? Maybe you play sports together or video games. Perhaps they are friends you can only spend time with in school.

Have you ever asked your friend if they know if they are going to heaven and trust Jesus as their Savior? Jesus died on the cross to pay for all sin, but a person has to believe in His payment to be saved. People cannot believe in something that they haven't heard about. Winning souls is active. We have to talk to others so that they can trust Jesus and go to heaven someday.

You might be afraid to talk to others about Jesus, but talking about Christ is what saves people. Maybe you can invite them to attend church with you or another Christian activity.

Think about how happy your friends would be if they trusted Christ as their Savior if they already hadn't. Let our feet be the ones that bring the gospel to others.

† † † † †

Dear Jesus,

I want my friends to trust You as their Savior. Help me to talk to them about You. Let my feet be the ones that bring the gospel to my friend.

Amen.

Should you tell your friends about Jesus and how He died on the cross to pay for their sins, and salvation is free?

Make a list below of the people you would like to tell about Jesus. They could be family members or friends.

34. GARDEN - WEED

My Father above
   Made the trees
And the flowers
   That feed the bees.

He made the grass
   For cows to feed
And my garden
   Full of weed.

I pulled them out
   One by one,
Didn't rest till,
   My work was done.

"I went past the field of a sluggard, past the vineyard of someone who has no sense; thorns had come up everywhere, the ground was covered with weeds, and the stone wall was in ruins. I applied by heart to what I observed and learned a lesson from what I saw: A little sleep, a little slumber, a little folding of the hands to rest – and poverty will come on you like a thief and scarcity like an armed man." (Proverbs 24:30-34)

† † † † †

Have you ever had a garden with lots of beautiful flowers, plants, or vegetables? It takes a lot of work to keep your garden looking beautiful. Unfortunately, weeds start growing, and you have to pull them out. To have our flower garden looking beautiful, we have to keep pulling the weeds out.

Maybe you get tired of pulling out the weeds, so you quit weeding. Before you know it, the weeds have overtaken the garden, and they choke out the plants. Now your beautiful flower garden doesn't look so lovely.

That is the same way about us. If we sit back and do nothing, then life will pass us by. You have choices to make, to do nothing, or to accomplish things. To have a good life, you should do your school work and study for your tests. You can't sit back and do nothing and expect to make good grades.

Jesus wants us to enjoy life. It is OK to take time and have fun. You can play at the beach or in the forest, and play sports and games with your friends. But He doesn't want kids to be lazy but accomplish goals in life.

Dear Jesus,

Help me not to be a sluggard in life. Help me to do well in school and to accomplish things.

Amen.

What do the verses above say about the sluggard?

List below some of the responsibilities you have.

35. MY CAT

Of all the animals in the land
   I think my cats the best,
And because she's in my life
   I am so very blessed.

Early in the morning
   She jumps up on my feet,
And then we play together
   Until it's time to eat.

Sometimes when I'm sad,
   And can't go out to play,
She lays upon my lap
   And brightens up my day.

And when the day is over,
   And I'm tucked inside my bed,
She purrs goodnight to me,
   And sleeps beside my head.

"The wolf will live with the lamb, the leopard will lie down with the goat, the calf and the lion and the yearling together; and a little child will lead them. The cow will feed with the bear, their young will lie down together, and the lion will eat straw like the ox." (Isaiah 11:6,7)

† † † † †

Do you have a pet cat or dog? Have you ever wanted to cuddle up to a big lion or tiger? I have. The verses above are talking about when children can cuddle with a lion or tiger, during the millennium.

Some people believe that the world is going to end soon. That is not what the Bible says. The Bible tells us that there is going to be a one-thousand-year reign of Christ on the earth. After that, God will create a new heaven and earth. We don't know what that will be like, but we will be with Jesus.

The millennium is the time when Christ comes back to earth and reigns for 1,000 years. The Bible tells us that the next major event that will happen on earth is the tribulation, which will last for seven years. After the seven years of tribulation, Jesus will come back to earth and set up his kingdom.

For almost 1,000 years, there will be no wars on earth but peace. We don't know when the tribulation is coming, and after that, the millennium, but it is sometime in the future.

The animals were peaceful in the garden of Eden, but when Adam and Eve sinned, everything changed. God will make them tame again during the millennium. Then everything will be peaceful, and children can play with the lions and tigers.

† † † † †

Dear Jesus,

Thank you for giving us pets that we can love and take care of. I know that You will reign for one-thousand-years on the earth and that the world will not end soon. Thank You for taking care of me.

Amen.

What will happen during the millennium?

If you have a pet, write below some of the things you enjoy doing with them.

36. WALKING IN THE WOODS

I love to walk in the woods,
　　Where the trees are big and tall,
And seeing different colors
　　As leaves changing in the fall.

Sometimes I come upon a stream,
　　Where I walk along its side,
There is a peace in the air
　　And I feel it deep inside.

I love to see the butterflies,
　　Or birds chirping as I walk,
I know God made everything
　　And to Him, I silently talk.

"Oh, how I love your law! I meditate on it all day long." (Psalm 119:97)

"May these words of my mouth and this meditation of my heart be pleasing in Your sight, Lord, my Rock and my Redeemer." (Psalm 19:14)

† † † † †

When you hear the word 'meditation' what comes to your mind? There are different types of meditation.

When some people think of meditation, they think it is some kind of mysticism where a person sits in unusual positions. They may make humming noises and clear their mind of everything. But that is not what the Bible means when it mentions meditation.

What is Christian meditation? Above are two verses that mention it in the Bible. Christian meditation is founded on the Bible and reveals the Lord to us. It is an active thought process where we study the word of God and apply it to our lives.

We can also meditate on nature thinking about how awesome the Lord is. When we look at the mountains, oceans, forests, and dwell upon the power of God. When we observe small flowers or insects and think about how intricate God created everything, we are meditating on Him.

God created us and wants to have a relationship with each of us. He created the stars that shine at night and the sea creatures that glow in the depths of the ocean. We have an awesome God.

† † † † †

Dear Jesus,

Help me to read Your Bible, and dwell upon the words that tell about You. When I go outside in nature and see the things you created, help me to meditate on how awesome You are. Thank you for taking care of me.

Amen.

What are two types of Christian meditation?

Take time to go outside this week and write down all the wonderful things you see that God created.

37. CLOUDS

I saw a dragon in the clouds,
  His head so fierce and mean
Who swiftly turned into a horse
  His body so fast and lean.

Then over there I saw a cat,
  Whose mouth was open wide,
And I think I saw a little mouse
  Who quickly ran to hide.

Tomorrow I'll go out again,
  To see what the clouds may bring
For they are limited to my mind
  And can make almost anything.

"'I establish My covenant with you: Never again will all life be destroyed by the waters of a flood; never again will there be a flood to destroy the earth.' And God said, 'This is the sign of the covenant I am making between Me and you and every living creature with you, a covenant for all generations to come; I have set My rainbow in the clouds, and it will be the sign of the covenant between me and the earth. Whenever I bring clouds over the earth and the rainbow appears in the clouds, I will remember My covenant between Me and you and all living creatures of every kind. Never again will the waters become a flood to destroy all life, whenever the rainbow appears in the clouds, I will see it and remember the everlasting covenant between God and all living creatures of every kind on earth.'" (Genesis 9:11-16)

Do you enjoy going outside and laying on the grass and making characters out of the clouds? When I was young, I used to love looking at the clouds and seeing what pictures I could find. I still enjoy looking at the clouds and watch how they change their shape and appearance.

Do you like looking at rainbows? Have you ever seen a double rainbow?

After God saved Noah and his family from the flood in the ark, God told Noah He would never destroy the earth again with a flood. The rainbow represents God's covenant to us. A covenant is an agreement or promise that God has made to us, and God does not break His promises.

Dear Jesus,

Thank You for making clouds and rainbows for us to enjoy. Thank You for creating nature. Help me to enjoy the world that You created for us.

Amen.

What does the word 'covenant' mean?

This week look at the clouds in the sky. Write down in the space below all the different animals and things that you see.

38. THUNDER STORM

I saw the storm
  Coming my way,
One hot and humid
  Summer day.
The sky turned dark
  The clouds deep gray
Outside on the swing
  We could not play.
So, into the house
  We had to stay
Until the storm
  Passed far away.

"On that very day Noah and his sons, Shem, Ham and Japheth, together with his wife and the wives of his three sons, entered the ark. They had with them every wild animal according to its kind, all livestock according to their kinds, every creature that moves along the ground according to its kind, and every bird according to its kind, everything with wings. Pairs of all creatures that have the breath of life in them came to Noah and entered the ark. The animals going in were male and female of every living thing, as God had commanded Noah. The Lord shut him in. For forty days the flood kept coming on the earth, and as the waters increased they lifted the ark high above the earth." (Genesis 7:14-17)

† † † † †

God looked down at the people who He had created and saw that they were wicked. They were corrupt and very violent. God was not happy with the people He had created. God was only pleased with Noah and his family.

God told Noah to build an ark, and God told him how He wanted it made. It took Noah 120 years to build the ark. During that time,

Noah was preaching to the people to turn to God, but they didn't.

It had never rained on the earth before, so the people probably thought Noah was crazy to build a big ark on the ground.

God told Noah and his family to enter the ark. Even though it rained for 40 days and 40 nights, they were inside the ark for one year. After a year, the land was dry enough for all to leave the ark. God put a rainbow in the sky to promise Noah that He would never destroy the world again by a flood.

Dear Jesus,

Help me to be righteous like Noah. Help me to serve you, as Noah did. Thank You for sending the rainbow promising You would never destroy the earth again by a flood.

Amen.

Why did God save Noah from the flood?

Write below some of the things you enjoy doing when it rains outside.

39. SPLASHING IN PUDDLES

I love walking in the rain
And jumping over puddles
But some are much too large
And I end up in the muddle.

"As Jesus walked beside the Sea of Galilee, He saw Simon and his brother Andrew casting a net into the lake, for they were fishermen. "Come, follow Me," Jesus said, "and I will send you out to fish for people." At once they left their nets and followed Him." (Mark 1:16-18)

† † † † †

Have you ever played in rain puddles? Did you ever pretend to fish in a puddle? I did as a child.

One time my brother and I were both sick at the same time and had to stay home from school. We had screens on our windows that opened up, and there were bushes outside the window. We made poles out of hangers, put strings on them, and at the end put safety pins for hooks. I don't remember if we caught any leaves or not, but we had fun fishing.

Simon, who is also called Peter in the Bible, and Andrew were fishing one day. Jesus came along and told them to follow Him, and He would make them fishers of men. They immediately left their fishing boats and started following Jesus. What Jesus was talking about was soul winning.

There are many ways a person can learn

about Jesus. They can hear about him at church, or in Sunday school. They can learn about Jesus in books, the Bible, or on TV programs. They can also learn about Jesus from a friend.

Soul winning is when someone tells others about how Jesus died on the cross for their sins, and by believing in Jesus, they can have eternal life. Jesus wants all Christians to tell others about Him.

† † † † †

Dear Jesus,

I am glad that you died on the cross for my sins, and that I have trusted You for eternal life. There are people that haven't heard of you. Help me to tell others about You, that you love them, and that you died on the cross for their sins. Help me to be a fisher of men.

Amen.

Do you want to be a soul-winner and tell others about how Jesus died on the cross for their sins, and salvation is by faith?

Write below who can you tell about Jesus.

40. TEN COMMANDMENTS

1. You shall have no other gods before Me.
2. You shall make no idols.
3. You shall not take the name of the Lord your God in vain.
4. Keep the Sabbath day holy.
5. Honor your father and your mother.
6. You shall not murder.
7. You shall not commit adultery.
8. You shall not steal.
9. You shall not bear false witness against your neighbor.
10. You shall not covet.

There are 613 commandments in the Old Testament, and the Ten Commandments is a summary of them all. The first four commandments have to do with our relationship with God, and the last six have to do with our relationship with each other. You can read more in Exodus 20:1-17.

The Ten Commandments were written on two stone tablets by the finger of God and given to Moses on Mount Sinai.

God wants us to worship Him because He is the true God. None of the false idols that people worship can do what God does. False idols cannot hear, see, or speak. They cannot help people as Jesus does.

When asked what is the greatest commandment in the Law, "Jesus replied: 'Love the Lord your God with all your heart and with all your soul and with all your mind.' This is the first and greatest commandment. And the second is like it: 'Love your neighbor as yourself.' All the Law and the Prophets hang on these two commandments." (Matthew 22:37-40)

The Ten Commandments were not given to us as a means for individuals to get to heaven if they were kept. They were given to show us that we are all sinners and we can't work our way into heaven. Salvation is by faith in Jesus Christ.

The people living in the Old Testament were saved by faith by looking forward to Christ's death on the cross. Today we are saved by looking back on Jesus paying for our sins on the cross.

41. ANGER

I got so angry the other day
When my friend wouldn't come out to play.
"Why are you mean," to him I said
As my face turned shades of red.
"How can I build a fort in the tree,
If you won't come and play with me?"
Then my mom said, "your friend is ill,
You need to calm down and chill.
Getting angry is not good for you,
And it's not good for others, too.
Being angry and causing strife,
Is not something you want in life.
Now, deep breath and count to ten
Reset the moment and start again.
When you are calm, then you will see
Life is happier for you and me!"
So, I listened to mom and breathed deeply,
Counted to ten, and played happily.

"Get rid of all bitterness, rage and anger, brawling and slander, along with every form of malice. Be kind and compassionate to one another, forgiving each other, just as in Christ God forgave you." (Ephesians 4:31,32)

† † † † †

Have you ever been angry at someone and yelled at them? People will do things to us or say things about us, and we get upset or angry. Some of the ways we handle our anger are to yell or even throw things. Sometimes we will hear that someone said something bad about us, and we want to get back at them.

Everyone gets angry, what matters is how we handle that anger. Yelling at others is not what God wants us to do when we get upset. When we are upset, we should step back, take a deep breath, and think about what is going on.

There are two types of coping styles, aggressive and assertive. The aggressive style is yelling, arguing, and demanding you get your way. The assertiveness style is saying what you want in a nice way. It is defending yourself in a way that makes you feel good about yourself. It may take practice to say what you want in a positive way, but it will be worth it.

Jesus wants us to be kind to each other. We should treat others how we want to be treated. So next time you get angry, step back, take a deep breath, and think about what happened. Then consider if you should talk to your friend, or just let it go. Being kind is what Jesus wants.

† † † † †

Dear Jesus,

I know I shouldn't blow up at others when I get angry. Help me to handle my anger in a better way. Please help me to be kind to others as you want me to be.

Amen.

When you get angry, how do you handle your anger?

What do you think God wants you to do when you are angry?

Write below a time you were angry and how you handled the situation. Did you handle it well? If you could do it over again, what would you do differently?

42. NATURE

N ature is all around us
A bounding ever so
T rees are into forests –
U nderneath flowers grow
    And a
R ighteous God protects
E verything, you know.

"For since the creation of the world God's invisible qualities – His eternal power and divine nature – have been clearly seen, being understood from what has been made, so that people are without excuse." (Romans 1:20)

† † † † †

Do you ever wonder where the world came from? The majority of Christians believe that God created the heavens and the earth. When I was in middle school, I thought that God created the heavens and the earth. I also believed in evolution because I was taught it in school. You really can't accept both, but I never thought it through, and I believed in both.

There are many different types of evolution, and it keeps changing what it teaches. There is the big bang theory, but something cannot come out of nothing. Because we weren't there when the world was created, we have to take both creation or evolution by faith.

Faith in creation is based on facts and logic. There is design in nature, and God keeps everything running smoothly. The universe is so vast that we haven't discovered it all. It seems illogical that everything this huge came out of a tiny area.

We now know about DNA that wasn't previously known. There are so many new things that scientists have discovered to prove that there is design in nature, and objects are not thrown together by chance.

The verse above tells us that everyone can look outside and see the world God created, so they are without excuse.

Dear Jesus,

Thank you for creating the universe, the world, and me. You created the enormous stars that shine at night and the tiny cells in our body. Thank you for keeping the world running smoothly, the seasons, and food on our table.

Amen.

If you are interested in learning more about creation, many good books are written on the subject. It is good to read and increase your knowledge and faith in God.

ABOUT THE AUTHOR

Sandy Bohon is a Licensed Mental Health Counselor practicing in central Florida. She received her bachelor's degree from Florida Bible College and a Master of Counseling degree from Liberty University. In her spare time, Sandy enjoys spending time with her family, going to the beach and gardening. She has three adult children, three grandchildren and a rescue puppy, Bailey.

Other books by Sandy Bohon available on Amazon:
JOY in Overcoming Depression Through God's Word
JOY in Knowing Jesus Through God's Word
Poetry and Devotions for the SOUL

For more information please contact me:
sandybohonlmhc@gmail.com
And join my mailing list at:
www.sandybohonlmhc.com

If you enjoyed this book please leave a review on Amazon. Thanks!

Made in United States
Orlando, FL
07 December 2021